WORKBOOK

CONTEMPORARY ENGLISH
BOOK 4

Elizabeth Minicz

Kathryn Powell

Lydia Omori

CB
CONTEMPORARY BOOKS

a division of NTC/CONTEMPORARY PUBLISHING GROUP
Lincolnwood, Illinois USA

Cover Illustration: Regan Dunnick

Interior Illustrations: April Mosakowski

ISBN: 0-8092-0723-0

Published by Contemporary Books,
a division of NTC/Contemporary Publishing Group, Inc.
© 1999 NTC/Contemporary Publishing Group, Inc.,
4255 West Touhy Avenue, Lincolnwood (Chicago), Illinois 60646-1975 U.S.A.

Manufactured in the United States of America.

890 VP 0987654321

Contents

About the Workbooks

Contemporary English is a five-level interactive topic-based English-as-a-Second-Language series for adult learners ranging from the beginning-literacy level to the high-intermediate level. The *Contemporary English* Workbooks are designed for individual independent study as well as for classroom work. In the Workbooks, as in the Student Books, a predictable sequence is maintained.

For ease of use, the essential information in the **Spotlight** boxes of the Student Books is reproduced in the Workbooks. Each **Spotlight** is followed by a series of contextualized practice exercises, progressing from simple fill-ins to more challenging activities that ask students to use the target structures as they write answers to real-life questions about themselves. Answers to all Workbook activities can be found in the Teacher's Manual.

The **Read, Think, and Write** pages at the end of each Workbook unit synthesize skills presented and practiced in the unit in an engaging multi-stage activity. The reading is supported by pre- and post-reading questions. After the reading, one or two activities ask learners to organize the information, usually with the same type of graphic organizer used in **Wrap-Up** in the Student Book. The final problem-solving activity challenges learners to apply the content to their own lives. Each unit closes with a brief questionnaire, similar to **Think About Learning** in the Student Book, in which students note what was most enjoyable and helpful in the Workbook.

In short, the *Contemporary English* Workbooks provide the additional practice students need, in an easy-to-use, interesting format.

UNIT 1   LOOKING FOR THE RIGHT JOB

Spotlight on Present Perfect

I've been a packer before.

I haven't worked in a restaurant before.

Have they ever worked in a restaurant?

Use the present perfect to talk about things that happened at some time in the past. The time is not specific, and the action may have happened once or many times.

Practice 1

Complete the conversation with the present perfect either in short answer or question form of the verbs given. Use contractions wherever you can.

MS. POWELL: Let's see. You (1) *work* _____

_____ most of your career as a secretary?

SUSAN: Yes, that's right.

MS. POWELL: (2) *work* _____ you ever _____

as a supervisor?

SUSAN: No, I (3)_____ but I had a teacher's aide

when I taught for a year.

MS. POWELL: Oh, that's good. What kind of computer experience

(4) *get* _____ you _____?

SUSAN: Well, I (5) *do* _____ _____

mostly word processing.

Spotlight on Present Perfect Continuous with *For* and *Since*

How long **have you been working** at the factory?

I've been working here for eight months.
I've been working here since March.

Use the present perfect continuous (*have + been +* present participle) to talk about experiences that started in the past and are still continuing.

For describes a period of time (eight months, two years, five hours).
Since describes a specific starting point (March 1980, 2:00 P.M.).

Practice 2

Answer the questions with complete sentences. Use time expressions with *for* and *since*.

1. How long has the cook worked in this restaurant? (five years)

   _____

2. How long has Francisco been sending out résumés? (two months)

   _____

3. How long have Tom and Elida been in the housekeeping department? (May)

   _____

4. How long have you had the same boss (or teacher)? (your answer)

_____

5. How long have you been in this class? (your answer)

_____

Spotlight on Simple Past, Present Perfect, and Present Perfect Continuous

Simple Past	Present Perfect	Present Perfect Continuous
I had an interview yesterday.	**I've had** three interviews so far.	**I've been looking** for a new job since October.

Practice 3

Read John's résumé. Then answer the questions using the simple past or present perfect continuous.

John Kraft
1831 W. Clark Street, Apt. 4C
Evanston, IL 60201
847-555-8926

Objective: A responsible position as a shift supervisor with opportunity for growth.

Experience:

1995–Present *Shift Supervisor,* Will Electronics Company, Oak Park, IL Supervise 20 people assembling electronic components; train new workers; plan daily production goals; prepare weekly reports.

1993–1995 *Assembly Line Leader,* Brown Technology, Niles, IL Set up machines for product runs; coordinated supplies; troubleshot equipment problems.

1991–1993 *Assembly Worker,* Brown Technology, Niles, IL Assembled circuit boards; verified circuit board layout; followed assembly sequence job guide.

Education and Training:

1991–1993 Associates Degree from Niles College, Niles, IL Completed manufacturer's training course for the Cal-Technics 462 Soldering Machine at Brown Technology.

1. When did John graduate from college?_____

2. How long has he worked for Will Electronics Company?_____

3. How long has he been a supervisor? _____

4. When did he complete Cal-Technics training?_____

Practice 4

Complete the following interview questions. Use present, past, or present perfect where appropriate. Then write answers to your questions, using the same verb tense in the answer that you used in the question.

1. How long have you _____?

_____

2. Have you ever _____?

_____

3. When did you _____?

_____

4. What did you do _____?

_____

5. Can you tell me about _____?

_____

6. When are you _____?

_____

7. Do you know how to _____?

_____

8. How long did you _____?

_____

Read, Think, and Write

Interest Inventories: What kind of job is right for you? Your answers to an *interest inventory* will tell you about which *career clusters*, or groups of occupations, might be best for you. Then choose from a list of specific occupations.

Step 1: Circle how you feel about doing these things.

	SCORE			
	like a lot	like a little	dislike a little	dislike a lot
1. using tools, machines, math	4	3	2	1
2. measuring things, doing repetitive work	4	3	2	1
3. working outdoors in all kinds of weather	4	3	2	1
4. keeping records, working in an office	4	3	2	1
5. helping people, giving things they need	4	3	2	1

Step 2: Look at the sample career clusters and occupations. Each cluster corresponds to the five questions above. Which clusters got your highest scores?

Sample Career Clusters	Sample Occupations
1. Technology	carpenter, machine operator, engineer
2. Consumer Economics	baker, cook, dry cleaner, tailor
3. Outdoor	animal keeper, landscaper, nursery manager
4. Clerical	hotel clerk, receptionist, ticket agent
5. Service	hair stylist, nurse's aide, kindergarten teacher

Step 3: Now pick the three occupations you like best from Step 2. In your notebook put the most interesting job first. Is there another job not on the list that you're interested in? Write it below the first one in your notebook. In small groups, discuss your job choices.

Step 4: Go to the library to learn more about these jobs.

What skills and education do I need for these jobs?

Who can tell me more about these jobs?

Practice 5

In this unit, Pemba *networked* with a friend to find out about a job opening. How can you network? Think of people you know. Which ones might know about possible jobs (or know *other* people who might know)? Write names in the network map below.

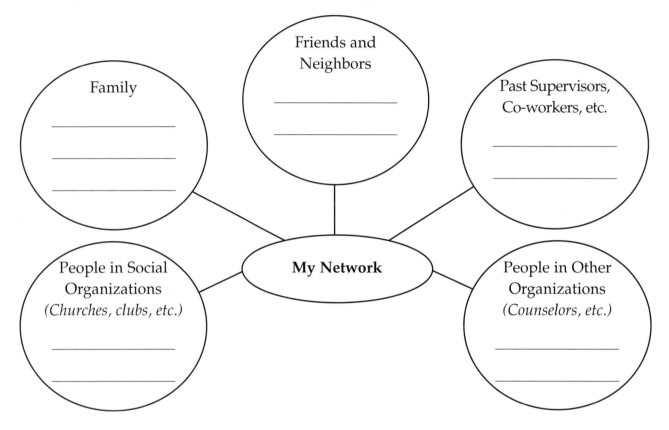

Practice 6

Now think about how you would ask these people about possible job openings. Write some ideas in your notebook. Try them out the next time you see these people!

CHECK YOUR LEARNING

What did you like best about this workbook unit? Why? _____

_____

What did you learn in this workbook unit to help you at work or in your personal life?

_____

_____

Spotlight on Reported Speech

Direct Speech

The flight attendant said, "The plane **has just landed.**"

The captain said, "The ferry **will be leaving** in five minutes."

Reported Speech

The flight attendant **said (that) the plane had just landed**.

The captain **told us (that) the ferry would be leaving in five minutes**.

Practice 1

In your notebook change the sentences from direct speech to reported speech. Don't forget to change the verbs and the pronouns.

1. Tim said, "I have to get a bus transfer from the driver."

2. The clerk said, "The train will be leaving in ten minutes."

3. My insurance agent said, "You need to get two copies of the report."

4. The travel agent said, "Bring a $200 deposit by Friday morning."

5. Jamal said, "I'm going back to Egypt."

Practice 2

Read the paragraph below. Answer the questions using reported speech.

Connie, Marc, and Bernard sat in the cafeteria at Toolmaster Corporation. They looked through the employee handbook. Connie said, "Let's see. I've been here six years already, so I get three weeks vacation. How about you, Marc?" Marc answered, "Hmm. Well, I've been here ten years, so I get four weeks. And I need it! What about you, Bernard?" Bernard said, "Boy! Are you two lucky! I'll be here two years next April, so I get two weeks off then. I want to take my family on a nice trip."

1. How many weeks of vacation did Connie say that she got?

_____

2. How many weeks of vacation did Marc say that he got?

_____

3. How many weeks of vacation did Bernard say that he got?

_____

Practice 3

Read the following dialogue heard on Flight 104. Answer the questions using reported speech.

A passenger said, "Excuse me. I'm not feeling well. My chest hurts."

The flight attendant answered, "Sir, I'll see if I can find a doctor on board."

1. What did the passenger say?

_____

2. What did the flight attendant say?

_____

Spotlight on Present Perfect

Ted **has** never **been** in an accident before.
Has Ted ever **had** an accident before? **No, he hasn't.**

I **have** just **spoken** to my insurance agent.
Have you **spoken** to your insurance agent? **Yes, I have.**

Use the present perfect (*have* + past participle) to talk about events and experiences at nonspecific times before the present time.

Practice 4

Read the list. Put a check next to the things you have done before.

_____ flown to another country   _____ had a car accident

_____ met someone at the airport   _____ called the police

_____ taken a bus trip to   _____ used a computer
another city

_____ taken a vacation   _____ ordered take-out food

_____ ridden on a ferry   _____ requested time off from work

_____ left a message on an   _____ sent a fax
answering machine

Practice 5

In your notebook write sentences about three of the things you have done.

Practice 6

Read the lists in Practice 4 again. Underline the things you have never done. Write sentences about three of those things.

Spotlight on Past Perfect

Event 1	Event 2

Ted and Tessa had planned to take a vacation before the car accident.

Event 1	Event 2

They both had requested three weeks off work before the accident.

Use the past perfect (*had* + past participle) when one event in the past happened before another event in the past.

Practice 7

Use the one event from each list below to write sentences about Ted and Tessa in your notebook. Use past perfect verbs.

Event 1	Event 2
1. waited at the airport	before plane landed
2. had stopped at a red light	when car hit them
3. spoken to an insurance agent	before he rented a car
4. requested a vacation	before he made travel plans
5. hadn't been afraid of driving	before the accident

Practice 8

Unscramble the groups of words and write sentences in your notebook.

1. called had/office the/times three/spoke before she/supervisor the to/Luz

2. had accident an had/was when she/work to driving/she

3. towed been had car/she and needed/work to ride a/her

Read, Think, and Write

Read this story about a good solution to a transportation problem.

Mr. J. K. Graves of Dubuque, Iowa, had an interesting solution to a transportation problem in 1882. Dubuque is in northeastern Iowa, on the Mississippi River. There are bluffs, or tall hills, along the Mississippi there.

Graves worked at the bottom of the bluffs, but lived at the top of the bluffs. All the businesses in town closed for lunch at noon every day for an hour and a half. It took Graves half an hour to get home, half an hour to eat, half an hour to take a nap, and another half hour to return to his bank, for a total of two hours.

Graves had seen incline railways, or cable cars, in Europe, and he decided to build one in Dubuque. On July 25, 1882, Graves used his cable car for the first time. His gardener operated the car, letting Graves down in the morning, up and down at noon, and up again after work.

Neighbors started asking for rides in the car, so Graves charged them five cents for a ride. The cable car burned down several times, and each time it was rebuilt. Visitors and residents of Dubuque can still ride the car, but now it costs $1.50 for a round-trip.

Source: Used with permission from Fenelon Place Elevator Co. Drawing by Susan Mahalick.

Practice 9

Write the answers to the questions on the lines below.

1. Who was J. K. Graves?_____

2. What was his problem? _____

3. How did Graves solve his problem? _____

_____

4 How long has the Fenelon Place Elevator been in use?_____

_____

5. How much does it cost to ride the elevator today? _____

Tell the story in your own words. Then write it in your notebook.

Practice 10

Think about transportation problems. Write two problems in
each box below.

My transportation problems	The United States' transportation problems
My community's transportation problems	My native country's transportation problems

Practice 11

In your notebook write a paragraph about one of the problems
from the window above.

CHECK YOUR LEARNING

What did you like best about this workbook unit? Why? _____

_____

What did you learn in this workbook unit to help you at work or in your personal life?

_____

Spotlight on the Passive Voice

Active	Passive
A volcano **destroyed** my village.	My village **was destroyed** by a volcano.
A hurricane **hit** the East Coast.	The East Coast **was hit** by a hurricane.

Use a form of *be* and the past participle of the verb to form the passive voice.

The phrase with *by*, sometimes called the agent, does not always appear.

Practice 1

Read the news story below. Decide if the verbs in the sentences are active (A) or passive (P). Underline the verbs. Write A or P on the line after each sentence.

Yesterday, hot rock, gas, and ash flowed from a volcano into Monserrat's capital, Plymouth. (1)____A____ A church, a clothing store, a supermarket, and a dozen houses were destroyed by fire. (2)_____ A government spokesperson said no one had injuries. (3)_____

This is the first time buildings in Plymouth were burned by the volcano. (4)_____ On June 25, burning ash and rock killed 19 people when lava flows swept through several villages. (5)_____ The volcano did not erupt for over 40 years until July of 1995. (6)_____ Plymouth has been abandoned by people most of the time since then. (7)_____ About 5,000 people used to live there. (8)_____

Practice 2

In your notebook, rewrite the sentences in Practice 1. Change the passive verbs to active verbs.

Practice 3

Read this newspaper story about the Soufriere Hills volcano on Monserrat.

$4,000 to Leave Homes

The British government is closing evacuation shelters on the island of Monserrat. The Soufriere Hills volcano continues to threaten the safety of the residents of this tiny island in the Caribbean. The volcano has already destroyed two-thirds of the island. Last year, residents left the capital city because of volcanic eruptions.

The government wants people to leave the island.

They are offering about $4,000 to every adult who leaves. Residents can have housing for three weeks on the nearby island of Antigua. Then they have to decide where to go next.

About 2,000 people are still living in temporary shelters on the island. The volcano killed 20 people in June. Monserrat is about the size of Washington, D.C.

Practice 4

In your notebook write the story in Practice 3 again, using your own words. Use passive verbs in your sentences when possible.

Practice 5

Look in a newspaper for several interesting stories. Underline the passive verbs in the stories. Copy three sentences with passive verbs in your notebook. Rewrite the sentences with active verbs if you can.

1. _____

2. _____

3. _____

Spotlight on Present Conditional

Condition	Result
If you live in the Midwest,	you can expect tornadoes.

OR

Result	Condition
You can expect tornadoes	if you live in the Midwest.
Assumption	**Condition**
You must not worry about tidal waves	if you live in Illinois.

Use the present conditional to talk about things that are true or possible. The most common way to begin a conditional clause is with the word *if*. Use the present tense in the *if* clause.

Practice 6

Match Column A with Column B.

Column A

1. If you live near a river, _____

2. If children don't get enough food to eat, _____

3. Don't be a volunteer _____

4. Go to an emergency shelter _____

5. You must have a lot of clothes _____

6. Your company must have good benefits _____

7. If you hear a tornado siren, _____

8. You must like books, _____

Column B

a. if you have a long vacation.

b. take shelter immediately.

c. if you have no place to live.

d. if you volunteer at the library.

e. you always worry about floods.

f. if you give so many away.

g. they starve to death.

h. if you don't have a lot of extra time.

Practice 7

Complete the sentences below with the present conditional.

1. If people have too much work to do, _____.

2. If employees buy their lunch every day, _____.

3. You must have good leadership skills _____.

4. If you have a lot of friends, _____.

5. You must speak English _____.

Spotlight on Conditional with *Would*

Unlikely or Untrue Conditions	Results
If I were a doctor,	I would volunteer in a free clinic.
Results	**Unlikely or Untrue Conditions**
I would give more money to charities	if I earned more money.

Use the counterfactual conditional to talk about things that are not true or not possible. Use *would*, *could*, and *might* in the result part of the sentence.

Practice 8

Read the lists below. Put a check mark next to the things you don't have.

_____ benefits at work   _____ a VCR   _____ a job I like

_____ three weeks of vacation _____ air conditioning   _____ a CD player

_____ a good paying job   _____ friendly neighbors

_____ a home computer   _____ cable TV

Practice 9

In your notebook write sentences with the conditional with *would* about what you would do if you had things from the list above.

Read, Think, and Write

Read the questions below the story. Then read the story carefully.

The Lifeline Express

Zelma Lazarus is the director of the Impact India foundation. On a plane trip from New York to Bombay, India, she was seated next to an Indian surgeon, Dr. Patrick Rosario. Dr. Rosario wanted to help people in rural areas of India with their medical problems. Impact India had a surgical van, and Ms. Lazarus offered to loan it to him. Then she also decided to go with him on a surgical tour.

It was very difficult for doctors to do surgery in the medical van because it was so small. One night, Ms. Lazarus watched the doctors operate on a young girl. They had to care for her for 24 hours in the small space. Ms. Lazarus heard a train in the distance. She had an idea. "If we had a train, we could go to more places."

Lazarus talked to the railway minister of India the next day. She told him about her dream. He thought it was a great idea and decided to give her three train cars. She needed about $300,000 to repair the cars. The U.S. Agency for International Development promised to give her $150,000. In just three months, Lazarus collected another $150,000.

On July 16, 1991, the world's first hospital train, Lifeline Express, left the train station in Bombay, India. The train took volunteer doctors to places without doctors. Every day, when the train stopped, 5,000 people came for help. In the last six years, about 100,000 people have been helped by the doctors on the medical train. Now Lazarus has another idea. She wants to develop a three-story hospital riverboat in Bangladesh.

Practice 10

Read the story again and answer the questions below.

1. Who is Zelma Lazarus? _____

2. What did Dr. Rosario want to do? _____

3. How did Zelma help Dr. Rosario? _____

4. What is the Lifeline Express? _____

5. What are Lazarus's plans for the future? _____

Practice 11

Think about these questions. Make some notes about your thoughts in your notebook.

1. Why do some people want to volunteer to help others?

2. How are people who volunteer different from people who don't volunteer?

3. What would happen if people didn't volunteer?

4. How have volunteers helped you or your family?

5. What are some things you'd like to volunteer to do?

Practice 12

Choose one of the questions above. Make an idea map in your notebook. Write your ideas in the circles.

Practice 13

Use your idea map to write a short paragraph in your notebook answering the question you chose in Practice 12.

CHECK YOUR LEARNING

What did you like best about this workbook unit? Why? _____

_____

What did you learn in this workbook unit to help you at work or in your personal life?

_____

_____

ALTERNATIVE MEDICINE AND HEALTHY LIVING

Spotlight on Gerunds

Living with allergies isn't easy.
Taking this medicine makes me sleepy.

A gerund is the *-ing* form of the verb that is used as a noun. You can use gerunds as the subject of a sentence.

You keep **getting** sick, don't you?
Have you thought of **trying** acupuncture?

Gerunds can also come after certain verbs or prepositions.

Practice 1

Use the gerund form of the verbs below to complete the sentences.
Use each one only once to make the best sentences.

| see | understand | pay | exercise | eat |

1. _____ your health insurance forms is not always easy.

2. _____ out is a favorite American activity.

3. _____ is very popular in the United States.

4. _____ for your own health insurance can be very expensive.

5. _____ your dentist for a check-up is important for your health.

Practice 2

Use the words below to complete the sentences.

| choosing | living | seeing | worrying | thinking |

1. Stop _____ negative thoughts!

2. Imagine _____ with no pain at all.

3. Consider _____ a vegetable dish instead of always ordering meat.

4. Stop _____ and learn to relax with yoga or breathing exercises.

5. You should consider _____ a chiropractor if you often have back pain.

Practice 3

Unscramble these words to make sentences with verbs followed by gerunds. Look for the punctuation.

1. before/pregnant./Women/smoking/they/are/quit/should

_____

2. Avoid/are/medicine/driving./this/when/you/taking

_____

3. doctor/medicines./asking/about/Consider /your/alternative

_____

4. acupuncture?/May/someone/does/I/who/suggest/seeing

_____

Spotlight on Infinitives

You need **to see** your primary doctor.
I decided **to talk** to my doctor about my medication.
I refused **to take** the medicine.
My doctor agreed **to change** the dosage.

Infinitives come after certain verbs.

The nurse told <u>me</u> **to make** an appointment.
She encouraged <u>me</u> **to ask** about alternative treatments.

When the verb involves another person, the noun or pronoun comes between the verb and the infinitive.

Practice 4

Use the infinitive forms of the verbs below to complete the sentences. Use each one only once to make the best sentences.

bring   get   learn   make   relax   see   speak   take

1. They teach you _____ in a Yoga class.

2. We want you _____ the names of all the medications you are taking.

3. Please ask _____ to a doctor if you have a question.

4. We promise _____ your visits to all of your doctors easier.

5. Don't forget _____ your doctor's referral form.

6. If you have problems with alcohol, the best thing is _____ help soon.

7. Remind me _____ all of my medicines on vacation.

8. Be sure _____ your doctor before you begin any exercise program.

Spotlight on Gerunds and Infinitives

Don't delay **getting** your flu shot!
I want to talk to a doctor instead of **listening** to a recording.

Some verbs (or prepositions) are followed by gerunds.

If you need **to order** a schedule of classes, press 3.

Other verbs are followed by infinitives.

I started **feeling** dizzy.
I started **to feel** dizzy.

Certain verbs can be followed by either a gerund or an infinitive.

Practice 5

Complete the sentences below with the gerund form of the verb.
Then write the sentence again in your notebook using the infinitive.

1. I hate *(fill)* _____ out insurance claim forms.

2. Tonia doesn't like *(have)* _____ to get a referral
   from her doctor.

3. Carol Anne likes *(cook)* _____ healthy meals for
   her family.

4. The nurse said she'll continue *(talk)* _____ about
   herbal medicines next week.

Practice 6

Write sentences that tell your feelings about doing things, using
hate, dislike, like, love and gerunds or infinitives.

1. _____

2. _____

3. _____

4. _____

Read, Think, and Write

Read the pamphlet carefully.

Check Up!

Understanding Your Health Care Benefits

What are the different kinds of health plans?

- The two main types of health plans are **HMO's** and **PPO's.**

What is an HMO?

- Health Maintenance Organization. It is a large system of medical services. HMO members go to specific doctors and hospitals, and they pay a certain, fixed amount. Routine, annual exams are usually free in an HMO.

What is a PPO?

- PPO means "Preferred Provider Organization." It is similar to an HMO because members pay fixed or very small amounts.

How are PPO's different from HMO's?

- PPO members can choose any doctor, but they may have to pay more. PPO's will usually pay 50–80% of services by doctors outside the network.

What else do I need to know?

- You may have to choose a primary care physician (PCP). He or she will be your main doctor.

What if I need to see a specialist?

- In an HMO, you will need a **referral** (permission) from your PCP. In a PPO, you can go directly to a specialist.

Practice 7

Read the pamphlet again and answer the questions below.

1. What is an HMO?_____

2. What is a PPO? _____

3. Would you choose an HMO or a PPO? Why? _____

_____

Practice 8

What do you worry about when you think of your health or your family's health? Write down the health issues you worry about in the idea map below. For example, are you worried about AIDS or cancer? If you have children, are they immunized? Are you worried about your parents' health?

Health issues I worry about

Practice 9

Now write a letter about the health issues you worry about. Use some of the sentence starters below. Bring the letter to a counselor, student advisor, or clinic to see if you can find solutions.

I'm worried about
I'm not sure how
I don't know if
I want to stop
I would like to start

I would like to know where
I'm interested in
I'm nervous about
I need
I plan

CHECK YOUR LEARNING

What did you like best about this workbook unit? Why? _____

_____

What did you learn in this workbook unit to help you at work or in your personal life?

_____

_____

Spotlight on Modals of Advice and Necessity

Advice

You **should** wait another two years before applying for citizenship.

You **ought to** take a citizenship class.

You'**d better** get some help.

Necessity

You **have to** be a permanent resident for five years.

You **must** be able to read, speak, and write English to pass the test.

You'**ve got** to find out where to take the exam.

Practice I

Complete the conversation. Use several of the modals above.

Tom: You want to pass the citizenship test, don't you? You

(1)_____ take a citizenship class.

Juan: What things do I (2)_____ know?

Tom: You (3)_____ know about the history of the

United States and the U.S. flag.

Juan: Will I (4)_____take an oath of allegiance?

Tom: Yes, you will. And you (5)_____ be at least

18 years old.

Practice 2

Imagine that you are a supervisor. What advice would you give a
new employee? Complete the sentences below.

1. You must_____.

2. You should never_____.

3. You've got to_____.

4. You have to _____.

Spotlight on Short Answers

Did you pass your citizenship test?	Yes, I **did.**
Are you working full-time?	Yes, I **am.**
Do you get benefits?	No, I **don't.**
Is that a problem for you?	Yes, it **is.**
Have you talked to your boss about it?	No, I **haven't.**

Practice 3

Write short answers to the following questions.

1. Did you see a Bulls game on TV this year?_____

2. Are you going to your native country for vacation? _____

3. Do you work at a restaurant? _____

4. Were you at a meeting this week? _____

5. Have you become a U.S. citizen yet? _____

Practice 4

Now write some new questions for these answers.

1. _____ Yes, I do.

2. _____ Yes, it is.

3. _____ No, it isn't.

4. _____ No, I don't.

5. _____ No, I haven't.

Spotlight on Tag Endings

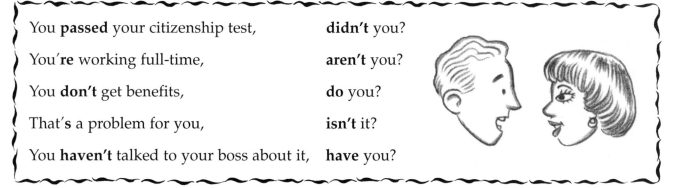

You **passed** your citizenship test,	**didn't** you?
You**'re** working full-time,	**aren't** you?
You **don't** get benefits,	**do** you?
That**'s** a problem for you,	**isn't** it?
You **haven't** talked to your boss about it,	**have** you?

Practice 5

Match Column A with Column B. Write the letters on the lines.

Column A

1. This is your first day here, _____

2. There's a vending machine back here, _____

3. You're new in this department, _____

4. We didn't start the new time sheets yet, _____

5. You haven't taken your vacation yet, _____

Column B

a. aren't you?

b. did we?

c. isn't it?

d. have you?

e. isn't there?

Practice 6

Read the questions below. Then rewrite them in your notebook using tag endings.

1. Is this your passport?

2. Do you need a visa now?

3. Are there three branches of government?

4. Did the President appoint those judges?

5. Was the citizenship interview difficult?

Practice 7

Complete the dialogues using modals of advice and necessity.

1. A. My daughter has the flu.

   B. She _____ stay home from school today.

2. A. Tom says there's a mistake on his paycheck.

   B. He _____ show it to his supervisor.

3. A. I don't know if I got the job yet or not.

   B. Maybe you _____ call and ask about it.

4. A. My husband likes working with the computers at work, but he sometimes has problems with them.

   B. He _____ find out if someone can help him.

5. A. Paula wants to work, but she's going back to Mexico in two months.

   B. She _____ apply at a temp agency.

Read, Think, and Write

Read the story carefully.

A Quick Summary of the U.S. Government

The U.S. government has three main branches: the Legislative, the Executive, and the Judicial. Each of the branches has specific powers and responsibilities, and the result is that no one branch has complete power. This is called a system of checks and balances.

The Legislative Branch *makes* laws. Another name for the Legislative Branch is Congress. The two parts of Congress are the Senate and the House of Representatives. There are 100 senators in the Senate, two from each of the 50 states. There are 435 representatives in the House of Representatives. The number of representatives from each state depends on that state's population. Senators have six-year terms, while representatives are elected every two years. Congress meets in the Capitol Building.

The Executive Branch *enforces* laws. This branch consists of the President, the Vice President, and the Cabinet (advisors). The President's term is four years. The Executive Branch works in the White House.

The Judicial Branch is the court system, which *interprets* laws. The Supreme Court is the highest court in the United States. There are nine Supreme Court justices. These judges are appointed by the President and serve for life. This part of the Judicial Branch works in the Supreme Court Building in Washington, D.C.

Practice 8

Using information from the reading, fill out the chart below.

	Executive Branch	Judicial Branch	Legislative Branch	
			Senate	House
Duties				
Who				
Where				
Term				

Practice 9

Think of *differences* between the U.S. government and the
government in your native country. Write them in the chart below.

The U.S. government

The government in my native country

Practice 10

In your notebook write a paragraph about the differences between
the governments in the two countries. Explain why you would or
wouldn't want to apply for U.S. citizenship. If possible, use modals
of advice and necessity, short answers, and tag endings.

CHECK YOUR LEARNING

What did you like best about this workbook unit? Why? _____

_____

What did you learn in this workbook unit to help you at work or in
your personal life?

_____

_____

UNIT 6   ENTERTAINMENT AND THE ARTS

Spotlight on Present Participles as Adjectives

The morning traffic is so **annoying.**
Morning traffic annoys (me).

Driving is very **tiring.**
Driving tires (me).

Present participles as adjectives describe nouns or
pronouns and *how they affect someone or something else.*
Often, the person or thing affected is not expressed.

Practice 1

Complete the sentences. Use each word only once.

annoying   exciting   thrilling   depressing

1. When the weather is cold and gray, it's very _____.

2. The roller coasters at Great America amusement park

   are _____.

3. Martin had a _____ day. He won $100.

4. I hate standing in lines! It's so _____.

Practice 2

Now use the adjectives in Practice 1 to write your own sentences.

1. _____

2. _____

3. _____

4. _____

Spotlight on Past Participles as Adjectives

Elena was **irritated** with her father.

Past participles as adjectives describe nouns or pronouns and *how they are affected by someone or something else.* Often, the cause of the condition is not expressed.

Practice 3

Write sentences using past participles as adjectives.

1. The audience/be/shock/when the dancer/fall down.

   _____ The audience was shocked when the dancer fell down. _____

2. Elena's mom/be/worry/when she/do not/call.

   _____

3. Robert/be/embarrass/when his car/do not/start.

   _____

4. Ed's grandmother/be/injure/in a car accident.

   _____

5. She/have/a/break/arm.

   _____

6. The young man/look/interest/when he hear/about the beautiful actress.

   _____

7. The students/be/disappoint/when the teacher/be/absent.

   _____

Spotlight on Participles as Adjectives

The dancers were beautiful and **entertaining.**
The audience was **entertained** for hours.

Present participles as adjectives describe nouns or
pronouns and *how they affect someone or something else.*
Often, the person or thing affected is not expressed.

Past participles as adjectives describe nouns or pronouns
and *how they are affected by someone or something else.*
Often, the cause of the condition is not expressed.

Practice 4

Complete the following sentences using participles as adjectives.

1. The movie was *(bore)*_____, so I fell asleep.

2. I felt *(bore)*_____ after two hours.

3. The dance was beautiful and *(please)*_____.

4. The audience was *(please)*_____ that the dance
   was beautiful.

5. Tim got *(confuse)*_____ when he had the
   wrong address.

6. The address was *(confuse)*_____ to him.

7. Linda thought the violence in the video was
   *(shock)*_____.

8. She was *(shock)*_____ at the violence.

9. The mystery novel was *(interest)*_____ right up
   to the very end.

10. I was *(interest)*_____ in the novel right up to the
    very end.

Practice 5

Read the following letter to a friend about a movie. Fill in the blanks with participles as adjectives for the verbs in the list below. Use each word only once.

confuse   surprise   amaze   exhaust   thrill   excite

Dear Amy,

I just saw the new movie, *Spacemen*. It was absolutely

(1)_____.

My favorite part was the (2)_____chase scene. It

began with four cars speeding down the expressway, but then it

changed into a foot race.

Tom Mays was running so fast that it made me

(3)_____ to watch him. I really enjoyed this movie,

but I felt a little (4)_____ during one short scene.

Five men were playing poker, but I couldn't understand who

was winning. Fortunately, the game is not important to the

main story.

Spacemen has a (5)_____ ending, and it was really

very (6)_____. Amy, you *must* see this movie! Let me

know what you think.

See you soon,
Rita

Practice 6

Now write sentences in your notebook about a movie, play, or game that you saw. Try to use participles as adjectives.

Read, Think, and Write

México's Dancing Ambassador Goes On Tour

The world famous Ballet Folklórico de México is touring the United States. Amalia Hernandez started the Ballet Folklórico in 1952. In 1997, she was 80 years old and still working with the dance company. Actually, there are two Ballet Folklórico dance companies. One dance company stays in México all year. The other is a touring group that travels around the world.

Amalia Hernandez started dancing when she was eight years old. She first became interested in dancing when her parents took her on vacations to small towns in México. Later she saw Russian ballet dancers and took classical ballet lessons. Amalia dreamed of combining Mexican folk dances with ballet. She developed dozens of ballets that are inspired by the dances from over 60 regions in México.

On this tour, audiences will see the performance of "Guelaguetza," featuring dances from seven regions of the state of Oaxaca. Men perform the Feather Dance from the Zapoteca region. Women perform a dance from the Mixteca culture.

Hernandez also started the Children's Cultural Education Fund in 1991. This project introduces over 30,000 schoolchildren in the United States to the Ballet Folklórico de México. It gives free performances and provides classroom materials.

Hernandez's two daughters are also interested in dancing. One daughter is a dancer and the other daughter trains dancers.

According to Amalia Hernandez, "Dance is a language that everybody understands."

Now answer the questions on the following page.

See the World Famous

Ballet Folklórico de México

Fun for the whole family
Saturday, June 27
and Sunday, June 28
at the Rosemont Theatre

Tickets go on sale
Monday, May 2 at the
Theater Box Office, or call
847-555-9098

Practice 7

Cross out the incorrect information in the sentences and write the correct information at the end of each sentence.

1. Amalia Hernandez started the Ballet Folklórico de México in ~~1997~~. 1952

2. The Ballet Folklórico only performs in México City.

3. The Ballet Folklórico has three touring groups that travel.

4. Amalia started dancing when she was on vacation with her parents.

5. The Children's Cultural Education Fund teaches Mexican children about dancing.

Practice 8

Think about the questions below. Then organize your thoughts and write them in an idea map in your notebook.

1. What did you want to be or do when you were a child?

2. What do you want to be or do now?

3. How have your plans changed? Why?

4. Do you think your plans will change again?

Practice 9

In your notebook use your idea map to write a paragraph about your past, present, and future plans.

CHECK YOUR LEARNING

What did you like best about this workbook unit? Why? _____

_____

What did you learn in this workbook unit to help you at work or in your personal life?

_____

Spotlight on Relative Clauses with *Who*

My friends met a man. He has his own seafood restaurant.
My friends met a man **who** has his own seafood restaurant.

Greg saw the tuna fisherman. He met him last night.
Greg saw the tuna fisherman **whom*** he met last night.

Relative clauses describe people or things. They begin with the
relative pronouns *who*, *which*, or *that*. Use *who* to describe people.

*In formal written English, use *whom* as an object pronoun.

Practice 1

Combine the sentences. Use relative clauses with *who*.

1. Robert has three cousins. They live in Vietnam and are fishermen.

   _____

2. Rosa talked to two people. They are going to the Caribbean on a cruise.

   _____

3. My friends know a man. He is starting his own company.

   _____

4. Eva had dinner with a friend. He is a job counselor at the community college.

   _____

Practice 2

Complete these sentences in your notebook.

1. Paul knew a man who . . .

2. The Andersons have a son who . . .

3. Tina has met some people who . . .

4. My teacher likes students who . . .

Spotlight on Relative Clauses with *Which* and *That*

Use relative clauses with *which* and *that* to describe things.

Paella is a delicious Spanish dish **that** has rice and seafood.

When the information in the clause is necessary to identify the thing, either word can be used.

Rod's company had a party on a beautiful lake, **which** is in Wisconsin.

When the information in the clause is not necessary, just additional, then *which* is used.

Mmmm

Practice 3

Match Column A with Column B. Write the letter on the line.
Use each letter only once.

Column A

1. Teresa took classes _____

2. Gina needs a loan to buy a car _____

3. The rains caused flooding _____

4. Chris found a crab cake recipe _____

5. The Clean River Coalition is a group _____

Column B

a. that lasted for five days.

b. which he used to make lunch.

c. that helped her learn Spanish.

d. which works to keep rivers clean.

e. which she found today.

Practice 4

In your notebook write sentences in the simple present.
Use relative clauses with *which* or *that*.

1. Jim/want/job/has health insurance

2. All fish/need/water/is not polluted

3. Sushi/is/Japanese food/has/raw (uncooked) fish

4. I/not/have/job/has a retirement plan

Spotlight on Word Order in Relative Clauses

A reporter is a person **who interviews people to get information.**

People **who like working with their hands** enjoy making things.

Relative clauses can come in the middle or at the end of a sentence.

Practice 5

Read the sentences below. Underline the relative clauses and circle the nouns they are describing.

1. People who live in Lafayette, Indiana, had to boil their drinking water this year.

2. Coliform bacteria, which were found in the water, can cause health problems for some people.

3. City workers drained the reservoir, which had to be cleaned.

4. Water that becomes polluted must be boiled before you drink it.

5. People who have questions about their water should call their local health officials.

Practice 6

Write about yourself. Use *who*, *that*, or *which*.

1. I like people _____.

2. I like jobs _____.

3. I don't understand people _____.

4. I enjoy weekends _____.

5. I like a boss _____.

Practice 7

Read the story below. Then underline the relative clauses and circle the nouns they are describing.

The Mountain God and the River God

Once upon a time in Vietnam, there was a beautiful princess who was the king's only daughter. Both the mountain god and the river god wanted to marry her, so the king said, "You two will fight, and the god who wins will marry the princess."

The two gods fought and fought with their bows and arrows. At last, the mountain god won and got to marry the beautiful princess. But the river god was a poor loser who became very angry and attacked the mountain. The river got higher and higher and covered the mountain. It rose up to the top where the mountain god and the princess lived. Then the mountain got higher too, so the river god could not get the princess.

That happened many many years ago. In Vietnam, there is a rainy season, which is in July and August. And even today, when the rains come there and the rivers rise, people say that the jealous river god is still trying to take away the princess.

Source: Adapted from "The Mountain God and the River God" from *Stories We Brought With Us,*

by Carol Kasser and Ann Silverman, © 1998. Reprinted by permission of Prentice-Hall, Inc., Upper Saddle River, NJ.

Practice 8

In your notebook unscramble the sentences about the story. Look for the punctuation.

1. The/won./married/god/princess/the/who

2. rain./has/Summer/the/season/is/most/which/the

3. god/say/the/People/river/that/jealous./is

4. lost/The/became/angry./god/very/who

Read, Think, and Write

Aquariums are popular places to learn about fish and other sea life.
Read this brochure for the North Carolina Aquarium on Roanoke Island.

Join the Aquarium Society!

Join the North Carolina Aquarium Society and receive a 10% discount on program activities. An aquarium membership gives you free admission to all three of North Carolina's aquariums, as well as the zoo in Asheboro.

Individual Memberships—$25.00
Family Memberships—$39.00

Summer Activity Highlights

Programs that have an asterisk (*) require advance registration. To register call the Aquarium at (919) 555-3494.

All About Sharks—Learn about the mysterious shark at one of our informative lectures. Sundays, Mondays, and Tuesdays at 11:00 A.M.

Beachcombing Biology—What did you find on the beach? Do you know what it is? Bring us your beach finds, and we'll identify them for you. Wednesdays at 1:00 P.M.

Ocean Jeopardy —Play our version of the popular TV game show. Test your knowledge of ocean facts and figures. Tuesdays, Thursdays, Saturdays, and Sundays at 1:00 P.M.

Marvelous Marine Animals —Learn about whales, dolphins, seals, and manatees. This program includes slides, film, and real exhibits. Mondays at 1:00 P.M.

*For Members Only** —Aquarium Society members can take special tours and attend special events. Limit 10. Fridays at 2:00 P.M.

Source: North Carolina Aquarium on Roanoke Island

Practice 9

Circle the correct answer to each question.

1. North Carolina has
   a. one aquarium.
   b. two aquariums.
   c. three aquariums.

2. A family membership costs
   a. $25.00.
   b. $25.00 per person.
   c. $39.00.

3. *Ocean Jeopardy* is
   a. a game.
   b. a slide show.
   c. a mammal.

4. The educational program about sharks is scheduled
   a. five days a week.
   b. three days a week.
   c. every day at 11:00.

5. To go to *For Members Only*, you
   a. must register in advance.
   b. pay a fee.
   c. register and pay a fee.

6. To find out about things you find on a beach, attend
   a. *Ocean Jeopardy.*
   b. *Beachcombing Biology.*
   c. *Marvelous Marine Mammals.*

Practice 10

Think about these questions. Then organize your thoughts and write them in the circles on an idea map in your notebook.

1. Is there an aquarium in your city? What is its name?

2. Have you or anyone in your family visited an aquarium? When?

3. If you haven't visited an aquarium, would you like to go to one? Why or why not?

4. Are aquariums important? Why or why not?

Practice 11

In your notebook write a short paragraph about why aquariums are important. Use relative clauses with *who, which*, and *that* if you can. Your idea map can help you organize your paragraph.

CHECK YOUR LEARNING

What did you like best about this workbook unit? Why? _____

_____

What did you learn in this workbook unit to help you at work or in your personal life?

_____

_____

UNIT 8 SAVING MONEY FOR THE FUTURE

Spotlight on Direct and Indirect Objects

The bank loaned **me** **money** for my new business.
    (indirect object)(direct object)

The direct object answers the question *what* or *who* receives the action. The indirect object tells *to whom* or *for whom* the direct object is intended.

Practice 1

Read the conversation. Underline the direct objects and circle the indirect objects. Not every sentence has objects.

Blanca: You're back! How was your vacation?

Esther: Great! Sorry I didn't send you a postcard. The beach

was perfect.

Blanca: I'm so jealous. I never have money for a vacation.

Esther: I started saving last year. I put money from my paycheck

into a savings account. The bank paid me interest, so I

made more money.

Blanca: That sounds easy, but I need all of my money

to pay bills.

Esther: You should put money in your savings first.

Practice 2

Look at the ways Blanca spent her money last month. Use the verbs below to write sentences with direct and indirect objects in your notebook.

loaned   bought   sent   gave

daughter: <u>new car</u>   mother: <u>$100</u>   church: <u>$10</u>   brother: <u>$250</u>

Spotlight on More Indirect Objects: Verbs with *to* and *for*

A: Who did you **give** your safety glasses **to**?
B: I **gave** them **to** Raul.

A: Who are you **writing** that note **for**?
B: I'm **writing** it **for** the second shift supervisor.

Many verbs are followed by *to* and *for* plus an indirect object.
Use *to* with these verbs: Use *for* with these verbs:

give	buy
hand	find
lend	get
make	

Practice 3

Complete each sentence with *to* or *for*.

1. Ursula made some Polish dumplings _____ everyone at work.

2. Sung found some safety gloves _____ Raul.

3. The team leader lent her ear protectors _____ Jean.

4. Piotr got a new safety belt _____ Maria.

5. Toshi handed a new insurance card _____ Victor.

Practice 4

You want to give some of your classmates special holiday gifts.
You can buy or make things. Write sentences about your gifts.
For example, write, "I'm going to make spring rolls for Boris."

1. _____

2. _____

3. _____

4. _____

Spotlight on Embedded Questions

Wh-Question	Embedded Question
S V	S V
Who has applications?	Do you know **who has applications?**

Embedded questions start with words like *who, how, what, where,* and *when.*
In some embedded questions, the word order is the same as in the *wh*-question.

V S	S V
What is a loan?	Please explain **what a loan is.**

In other embedded questions, the word order changes to *subject + verb* order.

Practice 5

Consuelo is a new employee who has a lot of questions.
Use her questions to create embedded questions for
the paragraph.

Consuelo doesn't know (1)_____ who her supervisor is. _____

She's not sure (2)_____. She

has no idea (3)_____ or

(4)_____. She doesn't know

(5)_____ She needs to talk

to the personnel office.

Practice 6

Last week, one of the workers cut his hand on a machine with
sharp blades. Consuelo helped to fill out the accident report.

Consuelo helped describe (1)_____ what the injury was _____

She wrote exactly (2)_____ and

(3)_____. She looked at the clock

and wrote down (4)_____.

Then she explained (5)_____.

1. What was the injury?
_____
2. What happened?
_____
_____
3. Who was there at the time?
_____
4. When did the accident take place?
_____
5. What help did the employee get?
_____

Spotlight on More Embedded Questions: Yes/No Questions and Infinitives

Yes/No Question	Embedded Question
Do I have enough money?	I don't know **whether/if I have enough money.**

Yes/No questions use *whether* or *if* in the embedded question.
Note that helping verbs like *do* and *did* are not used in the embedded question.

I'm not sure **whether I should borrow lots of money.**
I'm not sure **whether to borrow lots of money.**

You can also use an infinitive—the *to* form of the verb—when the meaning of the embedded question is *can* or *should*.

Practice 7

Laura works in a personnel office. She often answers questions for new employees. Complete the sentences below using embedded questions with infinitives.

Laura shows new employees (1)_____ how to fill out W-2 forms. _____

She tells them (2)_____ and helps

them decide (3)_____. She explains

(4)_____. Finally, she lets them know

(5)_____. The employees appreciate

her help.

1. How do I fill out W-2 forms?

2. When can I expect my first check?

3. Should I set up direct deposit?

4. How can I apply for benefits?

5. Should I buy safety shoes?

Practice 8

Zivko is setting up a job interview. He needs to ask some questions to make sure he knows where he's going. Complete his questions below using embedded questions. Use infinitives where you can.

1. What are the cross streets?   Could you tell me _____?

2. What routes should I take?   Do you know _____?

3. Where should I park?   Can you tell me _____?

Read, Think, and Write

Read the story carefully.

How the American Family Spends Its Money

How does the American family spend its paycheck? Here are some facts to think about. Most Americans have credit card balances each month. They owe money to the credit card company and pay the minimum amount. Three-quarters of Americans are in debt. Only one out of four people does not owe money. Most families have four-figure mortgage payments to make each month. That's over a thousand dollars.

Most American families *do* have some money to spend, however. The average family income is over $44,000. Of that, Americans spend about $32,000. That leaves some extra cash. In fact, two-thirds of Americans have extra money to spend. What do they do with that money? Fifty-five percent save money each year. Some are looking to the future. Twenty-seven percent of Americans have 401(k)-type retirement plans, where both the employee and the company contribute money to a retirement fund.

What exactly does the average American spend money on? According to the Consumer Price Index (CPI), the paycheck is divided according to the amounts shown on the pie chart.

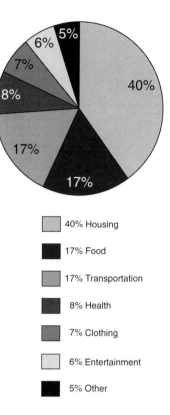

- 40% Housing
- 17% Food
- 17% Transportation
- 8% Health
- 7% Clothing
- 6% Entertainment
- 5% Other

Practice 9

Read each statement and circle *True* or *False*.

1. Most Americans have a credit card balance.   True   False

2. Only $\frac{1}{4}$ of Americans are in debt.   True   False

3. The average mortgage payment is less than $1,000.   True   False

4. Most Americans have extra money to spend.   True   False

5. Americans spend more on transportation and food together than on housing.   True   False

Practice 10

How do *you* spend your paycheck? Look at how Rhoun, Thi's friend, spends the family paycheck. Then fill out the chart for yourself.

	Rhoun	You
Housing	$800/mo.	
Food	$400/mo.	
Transportation	$300/mo.	
Health	$200/mo.	
Clothes	$100/mo.	
Entertainment	$100/mo.	
Savings	$100/mo.	
Total paycheck	$2,000/mo.	

Practice 11

In your notebook write a short paragraph about your money problems and plans for the future. How could you improve your budget, stretch your paycheck, and save more money? Use direct and indirect objects and embedded questions if you can.

CHECK YOUR LEARNING

What did you like best about this workbook unit? Why? _____

_____

What did you learn in this workbook unit to help you at work or in your personal life?

_____

_____

Getting Help in Your Community

Spotlight on Time Clauses

The manager seemed very friendly **while he was talking on the phone.**
  (main clause)   (time clause)

As soon as we walked into the office, things changed.
  (time clause)   (main clause)

Time clauses describe the main clause and answer the question *when?*
If the time clause comes first, use a comma.

Practice 1

Match Column A with Column B. Write the letter on the line.

Column A

1. John and I got married _____

2. Ever since my mom died, _____

3. The kids were outside playing _____

4. I always took the bus _____

5. When we first came to the United States, _____

Column B

a. we didn't speak English at all.

b. while I was making dinner.

c. when we were too young.

d. I've been so sad.

e. until I learned how to drive.

Practice 2

Complete the sentences below with main clauses and/or time clauses.

1. When I first came to this class, _____.

2. After my family _____.

3. Ever since I was a child, _____.

4. Before I _____.

Spotlight on Clauses of Cause/Effect

I smoke. My parents smoked.
I smoke **because my parents smoked.**
(effect)   (cause)

You can use *because* and *since* to combine two separate sentences.

They smoked. I thought it was OK.
Since they smoked, I thought it was OK.
     (cause)   (effect)

Because and *since* always begin the "cause" part of the sentence.

Practice 3

Use *because* or *since* to combine each pair of sentences below.
Don't change the order of the sentences. Pay attention to the
punctuation. Be careful! Which is cause, and which is effect?

1. Some people have problems. They are poor.

   _____ Some people have problems because they are poor. _____

2. They are fighting to survive. They don't have time for education.

   _____

3. They can't find good jobs. They don't have a good education.

   _____

4. They can't find good jobs. They feel frustrated.

   _____

5. They rob or steal. They have to pay for their needs.

   _____

Practice 4

Think of some other community problems that are *cyclical* (one bad thing leads to another bad thing). In your notebook, write cause/effect sentences with *because* or *since*. You can write about problems in the United States or in your native country.

Spotlight on Clauses of Opposition

Some smokers smoke only one or two cigarettes daily, **while others smoke two or three packs a day.**

Even though parents may want to smoke, they should remember that it might harm their kids too.

Clauses of opposition are used to contrast ideas, like the word *but*. The opposition clause can come at the beginning or the end of the sentence.

You can use *while, whereas, though, although,* and *even though* to begin a clause of opposition.

Practice 5

Use the adverbs below to complete the sentences. Use each adverb only once. Some sentences have more than one correct answer.

though   while   even though   although   whereas

1. I guess I should quit smoking _____ I only smoke one or two cigarettes a day.

2. _____ many smokers want to quit smoking, they many need to try five or six times before they completely stop.

3. Smoking is not allowed in restaurants in California, _____ it is allowed in most other states.

4. Some smokers try to quit smoking by joining support groups like Nicotine Anonymous,_____ others try to quit by themselves.

5. _____ smokers can buy nicotine gum or a skin patch to help them quit, the main key to success is being ready to quit.

Spotlight on Adverb Clauses: Review

Time	Cause/Effect	Opposition
before . . .	because . . .	while . . .
after . . .	since . . .	though . . .
when(ever) . . .	now that . . .	even though . . .
while . . .		although . . .
by the time . . .		

Practice 6

Read the story below. Then complete it with the word(s) in the grammar box above. Some words may be used several times, and some may not be used at all.

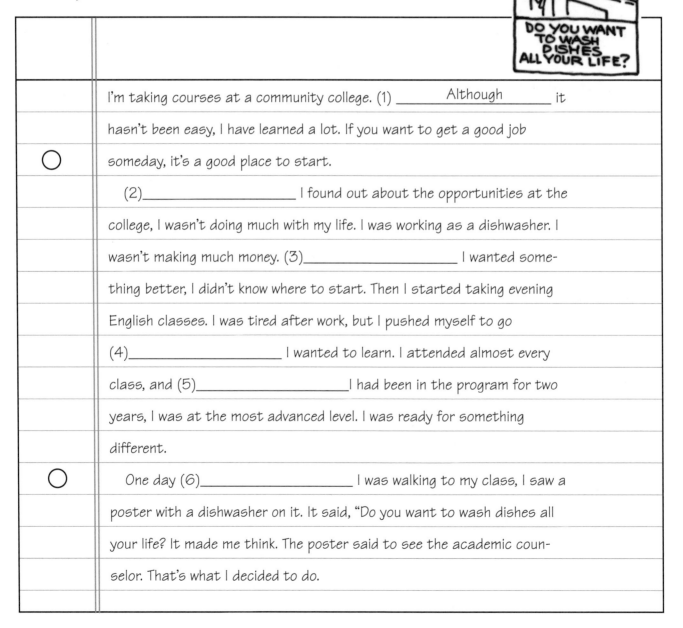

DO YOU WANT TO WASH DISHES ALL YOUR LIFE?

I'm taking courses at a community college. (1) _____Although_____ it hasn't been easy, I have learned a lot. If you want to get a good job someday, it's a good place to start.

(2)_____ I found out about the opportunities at the college, I wasn't doing much with my life. I was working as a dishwasher. I wasn't making much money. (3)_____ I wanted some-thing better, I didn't know where to start. Then I started taking evening English classes. I was tired after work, but I pushed myself to go (4)_____ I wanted to learn. I attended almost every class, and (5)_____ I had been in the program for two years, I was at the most advanced level. I was ready for something different.

One day (6)_____ I was walking to my class, I saw a poster with a dishwasher on it. It said, "Do you want to wash dishes all your life? It made me think. The poster said to see the academic coun-selor. That's what I decided to do.

Read, Think, and Write

Look at the yellow pages. Then read the questions below.

CHILD-COMPUTERS

CHILD CARE

Beth's Tot Day Care
  106 Meadow St Elm Gr............012-0723
Children's Learning Center
  13 Highland Av Newtown.........555-9336
CHILDREN'S & INFANTS' WEAR
Kidz Klothes
  49 Cedar Dr Newtown.............555-8060
CHIMNEY CLEANING
Clean Sweeps Inc
  1400 Oak St Waterville...........123-2888
Kharfen Chimney Service
  10 Mt Vernon Auburn.............123-9087
CHIROPRACTIC PHYSICIANS
Auburn Chiropractic
  112 Mt Vernon Auburn...........123-7994

CLEANERS
J-P Dry Cleaning
  1245 Oak St Waterville...........037-3861
One Hour Cleaners
  43 Crest Dr Newtown.............123-3729
CLINICS & MEDICAL CENTERS
Family Medical Center
  74 Forest St Woodale.............012-7390
Waterville Medical Center
  30 Brockway Waterville...........123-8002
CLUBS
Elm Grove Fitness Club
  345 Meadow St Elm Gr..........012-4434
Waterville Golf Club
  124 Somerset Rd Waterville..537-2987
COMPUTERS & EQUIP.- DEALERS
Comp-U-Save Inc
  288 Main St Elm Gr............012-2363
Computer Service Center
  45 Otis Av Auburn..................555-7080

Practice 7

Write the name of the place where these people should go.

1. Linda lives in Newtown, and she needs someone to take care of
   her two-year-old while she works.

   She should go to __Children's Learning Center__.

2. Seth lives in Elm Grove. He wants to have e-mail at home.
   He needs to find out how much modems cost.

   He should go to _____.

3. Stephan lives in Waterville. He's having chest pains. He's worried.

   He should go to _____.

4. Elia has gained weight, and he wants to get into good shape.

   He should go to _____.

Practice 8

Think of the community resources in your own town. Imagine that a family from a different country is going to move to your town. They have no place to live, no jobs, and small children. Use your telephone directory to help them find what they need.

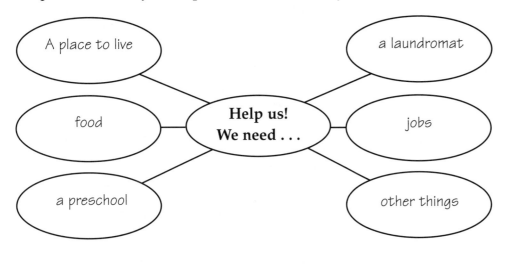

Practice 9

In your notebook write a short letter to the family. Give them advice about where they should go and what they should do when they get there. If possible, use clauses of time, cause/effect, and opposition.

CHECK YOUR LEARNING

What did you like best about this workbook unit? Why? _____

_____

What did you learn in this workbook unit to help you at work or in your personal life?

_____

_____

Spotlight on Conditional with *Will*

Action	Possible Consequence
If the electricity goes off,	you'll have to reset your alarm clock.

Possible Consequence	Action
You'll have to reset your alarm clock	if the electricity goes off.

Use future conditional to talk about things that may happen in the future, including actions and possible consequences.

Practice 1

Complete the conversation. Use the conditional with *will* and the verbs below.

arrive   be   drive   get   have   leave

Dave: What time do we have to leave tonight, Susan?

Susan: If we (1)_____ at 8:00, we (2)_____ at the party at 8:30. I don't want to be later than that.

Dave: OK. If I (3)_____ home from work by 7:30, I (4)_____ time to take a shower and change before we leave. What time is the baby-sitter coming?

Susan: She (5)_____ here at 7:45 if her parents (6)_____ her over.

Practice 2

Carlos just got a new job at Direx, Inc. Complete these sentences about him.

1. If Carlos forgets to punch the time clock, _____his pay will be docked_____.

2. If he learns how to use a computer, he _____.

3. He will quit his job if _____.

4. He will join an HMO if _____.

5. If he becomes a team leader, _____.

6. Carlos will take a vacation to Bolivia if _____.

7. If he works overtime, _____.

8. His boss will leave a message on Carlos's answering machine if _____

_____.

Practice 3

Match the ideas in the two columns to make logical sentences using the conditional with *will*. Write them on the lines.

1. eat dinner too late	a. save money
2. buy too many things on credit	b. come home exhausted
3. shop carefully	c. learn English faster
4. have two jobs and go to school	d. have trouble sleeping
5. watch TV and listen to the radio in English	e. have to pay high interest

1. _____

2. _____

3. _____

4. _____

5. _____

Spotlight on Phrasal Verbs

Inseparable	Separable
Run into a friend.	**Pay back** the money.
	Pay the money **back**.
	Pay it **back**.

Many phrasal verbs are separable. A noun can come between the two parts. If you use a pronoun, it must come between the two parts. Other phrasal verbs are never separated. You must memorize which verbs are separable.

Practice 4

Roberto's wife wrote this paragraph about her ESL class.
Complete it with these phrasal verbs.

bring out   call up   plug in   put away   turn on   wipe off

We are learning classroom management. At the beginning of class

(1)_____ the VCR and (2)_____ it

_____. At the end of class, we (3)_____ the

books and (4)_____ the board.

We have to (5)_____ the school if we cannot come to class.

Practice 5

Read the sentences. Then rewrite them in your notebook, replacing the underlined words with pronouns. Some of the verbs are separable, and some are not.

1. I ran into <u>my friends</u> at the supermarket.

2. Look out for <u>your brother</u>.

3. Pick up <u>the groceries.</u>

4. When did you get over <u>the flu</u>?

5. How well do you get along with <u>your co-workers</u>?

Practice 6

Luis is training a new employee. Read his tips for working in the bakery. Complete the tips with phrasal verbs below. Use the definitions if you need help.

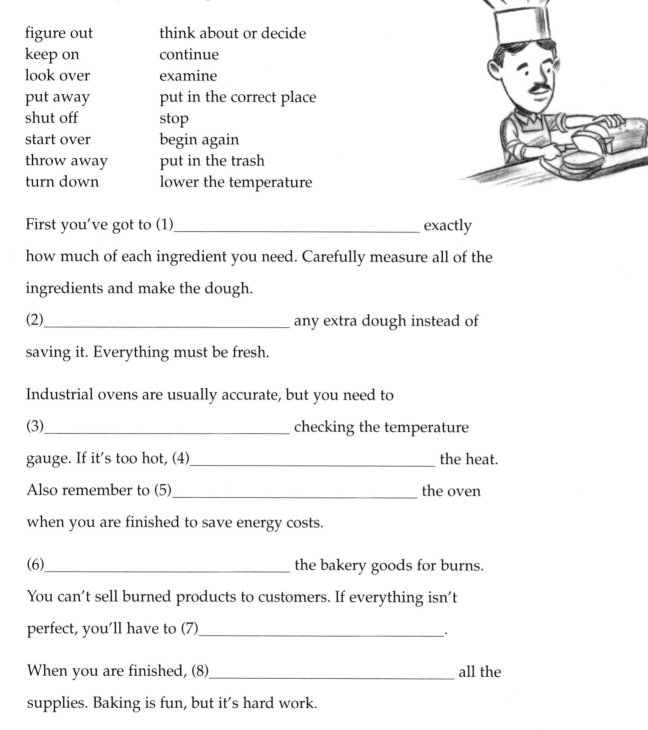

figure out	think about or decide
keep on	continue
look over	examine
put away	put in the correct place
shut off	stop
start over	begin again
throw away	put in the trash
turn down	lower the temperature

First you've got to (1)_____ exactly

how much of each ingredient you need. Carefully measure all of the

ingredients and make the dough.

(2)_____ any extra dough instead of

saving it. Everything must be fresh.

Industrial ovens are usually accurate, but you need to

(3)_____ checking the temperature

gauge. If it's too hot, (4)_____ the heat.

Also remember to (5)_____ the oven

when you are finished to save energy costs.

(6)_____ the bakery goods for burns.

You can't sell burned products to customers. If everything isn't

perfect, you'll have to (7)_____.

When you are finished, (8)_____ all the

supplies. Baking is fun, but it's hard work.

Read, Think, and Write

Read the story carefully.

I'm Only a Beep Away

One out of eight people in the United States has a beeper, or a pager. How helpful are beepers? Here are the stories of three people who have beepers. Decide how helpful beepers are to them.

Alejandro earns $6.00 an hour. He shares an apartment with three roommates. One of his roommates never paid his share of the telephone bill. The telephone company disconnected the phone for nonpayment. Now Alejandro has a **numeric beeper.** If someone wants to talk to him, they call his beeper and leave a telephone number, and he calls them back. Alejandro's beeper cost him $65.00, and the monthly service fee is $8.00.

Alicia has three kids ages 10–15. She works two jobs, and she isn't home a lot. She worries about her kids. Alicia bought an **alphanumeric pager.** When her kids need her, they call an operator, who leaves a typed message on Alicia's pager. The pager cost $150.00 and the monthly fee is $25.00. Her kids are just a message away!

Carina is a sales representative for a medical supply company. She spends most of her day calling on customers. She used to have a cellular phone, but it was a problem. Often she got calls when she was trying to talk to customers. Now Carina has a **voice mail beeper.** Callers can leave messages up to four minutes long. Carina's employer paid for the $300.00 beeper. They also pay the monthly fee of $45.00.

Practice 7

Read the story again and fill in the chart below.

Pager Type	Cost	How It Works	Advantages	Disadvantages

Practice 8

Think about these questions. Organize your thoughts. Make an idea map in your notebook. Write your ideas in the circles.

1. Why do so many people have beepers?

2. Do you have a pager or beeper? Why?

3. If you don't have a beeper, do you want one? Why or why not?

4. What are the advantages of having a beeper?

5. What are the disadvantages of having a beeper?

Practice 9

In your notebook write a short paragraph about how beepers can improve your life. Explain their advantages and disadvantages. Your idea map can help you organize your paragraph.

CHECK YOUR LEARNING

What did you like best about this workbook unit? Why? _____

_____

What did you learn in this workbook unit to help you at work or in your personal life?

_____

_____